Counting

Key Stage 1
For ages 5-7

Practise & Learn

Published by CGP

Editors:
Joe Brazier
Charlotte Burrows

Updated by Rob Harrison and Ruth Wilbourne

With thanks to Simon Little for the proofreading.

ISBN: 978 1 84762 983 8

With thanks to Laura Jakubowski for the copyright research.
With thanks to iStockphoto.com for permission to reproduce the photographs used on pages 28 and 29.

Printed by Elanders Ltd, Newcastle upon Tyne
Clipart from Corel®

Contents

Numbers and Words

You can write numbers as figures or words.

0	zero	6	six	34	thirty-four
1	one	7	seven	42	forty-two
2	two	8	eight	53	fifty-three
3	three	9	nine	67	sixty-seven
4	four	10	ten	88	eighty-eight
5	five	17	seventeen	100	one hundred

Draw lines to match the words and numbers.

thirty   **ten**   **zero**

6

12   **10**   **21**   **18**

six   **30**   **twelve**   **0**

twenty-one   **eighteen**

Write these numbers as words.

3 <u>t h r e e</u>

8 _ _ _ _ _

1 _ _ _

4 _ _ _ _

9 _ _ _ _

17 _ _ _ _ _ _ _ _ _

11 _ _ _ _ _ _

15 _ _ _ _ _ _ _

20 _ _ _ _ _ _

16 _ _ _ _ _ _ _

Circle the number that matches the word.

eighty-seven

66 71 (87)

seventy-nine

44 79 97

ninety-three

93 55 39

one hundred

100 99 90

Place Value

The digits in a number have different values.

6 lots of ten
63
3 lots of one

1 lot of one hundred
0 lots of ten
102
2 lots of one

Write the answers to the questions in the boxes.

53

How many lots of ten are there? ☐

How many lots of one are there? ☐

Colour in the right numbers.

36   17   47   73   34

Colour in green the number that has 6 lots of one.

Colour in blue the number that has 4 lots of ten.

Colour in red the number that has 7 lots of ten.

6

Draw a line to match the description to the correct number.

4 lots of ten and 4 lots of one

5 lots of ten and 1 lot of one

8 lots of ten and 3 lots of one

8 lots of ten and 7 lots of one

9 lots of ten and 9 lots of one

Write how many lots of one hundred, ten and one there are in each number.

	hundreds	tens	ones
85 →	0	8	
106 →			
110 →			

7

Odd and Even Numbers

Numbers can be odd or even.

Even numbers end in 0, 2, 4, 6 or 8.

Here are some examples: 4   6   10   14   38   72

Odd numbers end in 1, 3, 5, 7 or 9.

Here are some examples: 3   5   11   13   45   69

Colour in the ice-creams that have even numbers.

Circle the flags that have odd numbers.

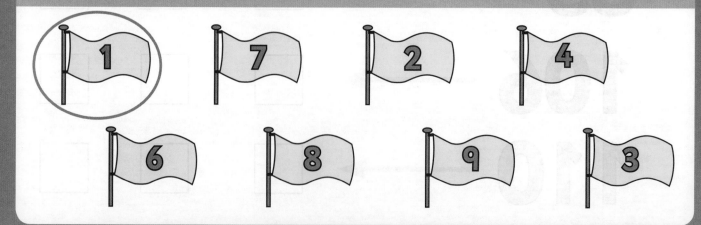

8

Write the numbers on the correct clipboards.

ODD

12 33 26 17 42 58 99 71 64

EVEN

12

Write the answers to the questions in the boxes.

51   66   78   73
  85   93   100   54

Which four numbers are even?

☐   ☐   ☐   ☐

Which four numbers are odd?

☐   ☐   ☐   ☐

Counting

Counting tells you how many of something there are. Here's an example.

There are [6] apples in this picture.

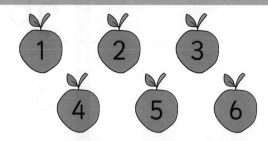

Write the answers to the questions in the boxes.

How many yellow balls are there? ☐

How many red balls are there? ☐

How many blue balls are there? ☐

How many green balls are there? ☐

How many balls are there altogether? ☐

How many stars are on the clown's side? ☐

Write the answers to the questions in the boxes.

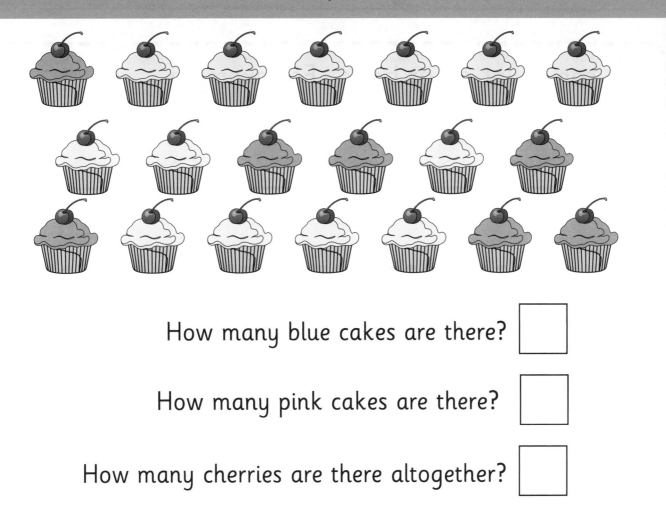

How many blue cakes are there?

How many pink cakes are there?

How many cherries are there altogether?

Colour in the right number of shapes.

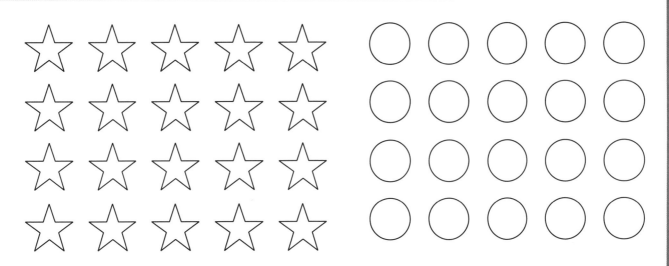

Colour in 15 stars.

Colour in 19 circles.

Counting On and Back

You can count on or back. For example:

Count on from zero to five.

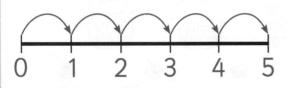

Count back from five to zero.

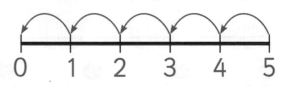

Use the number line to fill in the boxes below.

Count on from one.

| 1 | 2 | | | | |

Count back from ten.

| 10 | 9 | | | | |

Use the number line to fill in the boxes below.

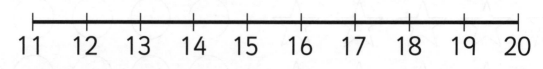

Count back from 19.

| 19 | | | | | |

Use the number lines to fill in the boxes below.

Count six on from 64.
What number have you counted up to?

Count three back from 71.
What number have you counted back to?

Count seven back from 86.
What number have you counted back to?

Count five on from 82.
What number have you counted up to?

Use the number line to answer the questions below.

Count on from 99 to 104. How many did you count?

Count back from 102 to 98. How many did you count?

Count back from 106 to 97. How many did you count?

Counting in Ones and Tens

You can count on or back in ones. You can also count on or back in tens. Here's an example.

Counting on in tens	10	20	30	40	50	60
Counting back in tens	60	50	40	30	20	10

Fill in the boxes with the missing numbers.

Starting at 12, count on in ones on the grid below. Colour in the squares as you go.

12	2	29	22	1	6
13	14	3	4	8	10
11	15	23	7	25	24
27	16	17	18	19	9
26	28	5	30	20	21

Count on in tens and write the missing numbers in the boxes.

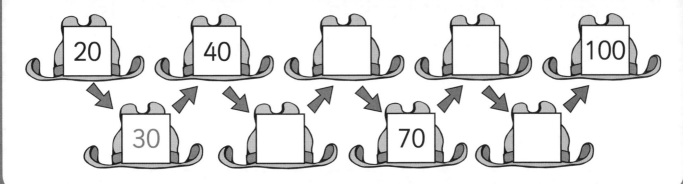

20 40 [ ] [ ] 100

30 [ ] 70 [ ]

Count back in tens and write the missing numbers in the boxes.

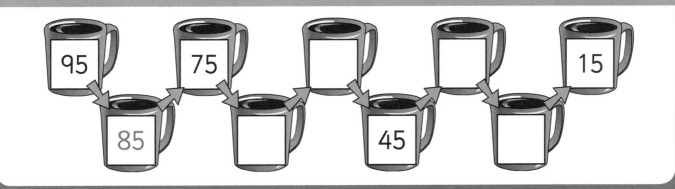

95 75 [ ] [ ] 15

85 [ ] 45 [ ]

Count on and back in tens from the numbers in the stars. Write the missing numbers in the boxes.

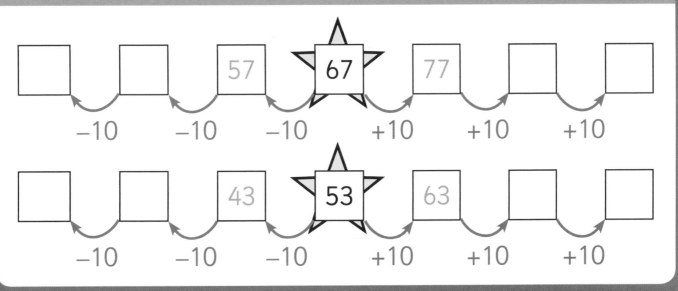

[ ] [ ] 57 67 77 [ ] [ ]
−10 −10 −10 +10 +10 +10

[ ] [ ] 43 53 63 [ ] [ ]
−10 −10 −10 +10 +10 +10

Counting in Twos and Fives

You can count on or back in twos. You can also count on or back in fives. Here's an example.

Counting on in twos

0	2	4	6	8	10	12

Counting back in twos

12	10	8	6	4	2	0

Count on in twos from 2.
Colour every stocking you land on.

Write the missing numbers in the boxes.

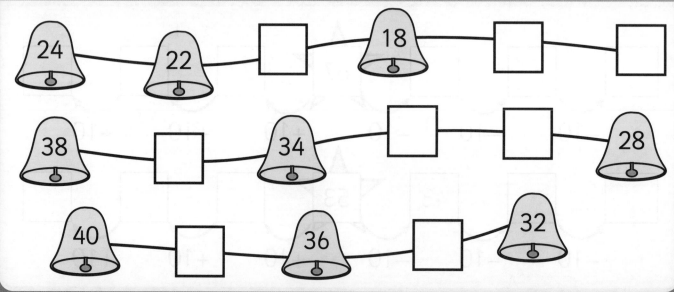

Practise and Learn

Counting

Ages 5-7

Answers

This section shows each of the pages from the book with the answers filled out.

The pages are laid out in the same way as the book itself, so the questions can be easily marked by you, or by your child.

There are also helpful learning tips with some of the pages.

4

Numbers and Words

You can write numbers as figures or words.

0	zero	6	six	34	thirty-four
1	one	7	seven	42	forty-two
2	two	8	eight	53	fifty-three
3	three	9	nine	67	sixty-seven
4	four	10	ten	88	eighty-eight
5	five	17	seventeen	100	one hundred

Draw lines to match the words and numbers.

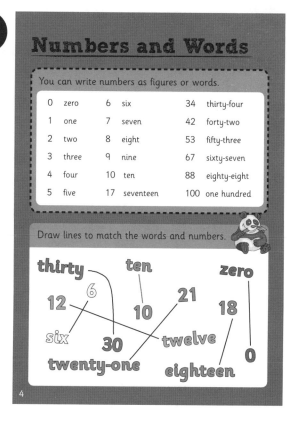

thirty   ten   zero

12   6   21   18

10

six   30   twelve   0

twenty-one   eighteen

4

5

Write these numbers as words.

3 t h r e e   17 s e v e n t e e n

8 e i g h t   11 e l e v e n

1 o n e   15 f i f t e e n

4 f o u r   20 t w e n t y

9 n i n e   16 s i x t e e n

Circle the number that matches the word.

eighty-seven   seventy-nine

66   71   **(87)**   44   **(79)**   97

ninety-three   one hundred

(93)   55   39   **(100)**   99   90

5

Place Value

The digits in a number have different values.

6 lots of ten

3 lots of one

63

1 lot of one hundred

0 lots of ten

2 lots of one

102

Write the answers to the questions in the boxes.

53

How many lots of ten are there? **5**

How many lots of one are there? **3**

Colour in the right numbers.

green
36 17 **47** **73** 34
blue red

Colour in green the number that has 6 lots of one.

Colour in blue the number that has 4 lots of ten.

Colour in red the number that has 7 lots of ten.

Draw a line to match the description to the correct number.

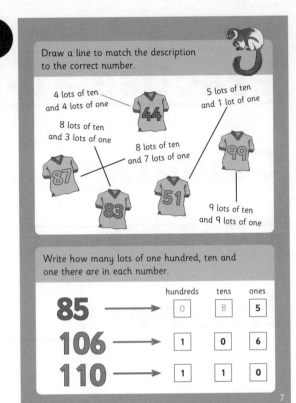

4 lots of ten and 4 lots of one

8 lots of ten and 3 lots of one

8 lots of ten and 7 lots of one

5 lots of ten and 1 lot of one

9 lots of ten and 9 lots of one

Write how many lots of one hundred, ten and one there are in each number.

	hundreds	tens	ones
85	0	8	5
106	1	0	6
110	1	1	0

For more practice, you can write down some numbers on a piece of paper and ask your child how many ones, tens and hundreds there are in each number.

Odd and Even Numbers

Numbers can be odd or even.
Even numbers end in 0, 2, 4, 6 or 8.
Here are some examples: 4 6 10 14 38 72

Odd numbers end in 1, 3, 5, 7 or 9.
Here are some examples: 3 5 11 13 45 69

Colour in the ice-creams that have even numbers.

0 1 2 3 4 5
6 7 8 9 10

Circle the flags that have odd numbers.

1 7 2 4
6 8 9 3

Write the numbers on the correct clipboards.

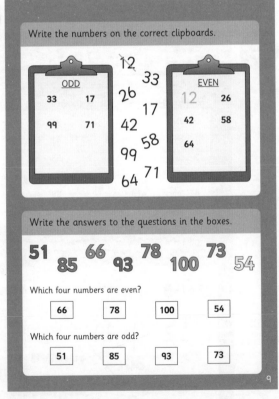

12 33 26 17 42 58 99 64 71

ODD
33 17
99 71

EVEN
12 26
42 58
64

Write the answers to the questions in the boxes.

51 85 66 93 78 100 73 54

Which four numbers are even?

66 **78** **100** **54**

Which four numbers are odd?

51 **85** **93** **73**

If your child has difficulty recognising bigger odd and even numbers, get them to practise writing out what odd and even numbers end in a few times.

10

Counting

Counting tells you how many of something there are. Here's an example.

There are [6] apples in this picture.

Write the answers to the questions in the boxes.

How many yellow balls are there? [1]

How many red balls are there? [2]

How many blue balls are there? [3]

How many green balls are there? [4]

How many balls are there altogether? [10]

How many stars are on the clown's side? [5]

10

To give your child extra practice at counting, ask them to count objects around the house — for example, how many apples there are in the fruit bowl.

11

Write the answers to the questions in the boxes.

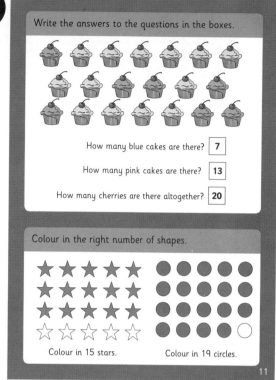

How many blue cakes are there? [7]

How many pink cakes are there? [13]

How many cherries are there altogether? [20]

Colour in the right number of shapes.

Colour in 15 stars.   Colour in 19 circles.

11

In the last question here, it doesn't matter which stars or circles your child colours in as long as they colour in the right number of them.

12

Counting On and Back

You can count on or back. For example:

Count on from zero to five.
0 1 2 3 4 5

Count back from five to zero.
0 1 2 3 4 5

Use the number line to fill in the boxes below.

0 1 2 3 4 5 6 7 8 9 10

Count on from one.

[1] [2] [3] [4] [5] [6]

Count back from ten.

[10] [9] [8] [7] [6] [5]

Use the number line to fill in the boxes below.

11 12 13 14 15 16 17 18 19 20

Count back from 19.

[19] [18] [17] [16] [15] [14] [13]

12

13

Use the number lines to fill in the boxes below.

62 63 64 65 66 67 68 69 70 71

Count six on from 64.
What number have you counted up to? [70]

Count three back from 71.
What number have you counted back to? [68]

79 80 81 82 83 84 85 86 87 88

Count seven back from 86.
What number have you counted back to? [79]

Count five on from 82.
What number have you counted up to? [87]

Use the number line to answer the questions below.

97 98 99 100 101 102 103 104 105 106

Count on from 99 to 104. How many did you count? [5]

Count back from 102 to 98. How many did you count? [4]

Count back from 106 to 97. How many did you count? [9]

13

For extra practice, you could ask your child to answer some similar questions without using a number line.

Counting in Ones and Tens

You can count on or back in ones. You can also count on or back in tens. Here's an example.

Counting on in tens	10	20	30	40	50	60
Counting back in tens	60	50	40	30	20	10

Fill in the boxes with the missing numbers.

Starting at 12, count on in ones on the grid below. Colour in the squares as you go.

12	2	29	22	1	6
13	14	3	4	8	10
11	15	23	7	25	24
27	16	17	18	19	9
26	28	5	30	20	21

Count on in tens and write the missing numbers in the boxes.

20   40   **60**   **80**   100
30   **50**   70   **90**

Count back in tens and write the missing numbers in the boxes.

95   75   **55**   **35**   15
85   **65**   45   **25**

Count on and back in tens from the numbers in the stars. Write the missing numbers in the boxes.

37	47	57	67	77	87	97
−10	−10	−10	+10	+10	+10	

23	33	43	53	63	73	83
−10	−10	−10	+10	+10	+10	

Counting in Twos and Fives

You can count on or back in twos. You can also count on or back in fives. Here's an example.

Counting on in twos	0	2	4	6	8	10	12
Counting back in twos	12	10	8	6	4	2	0

Count on in twos from 2.
Colour every stocking you land on.

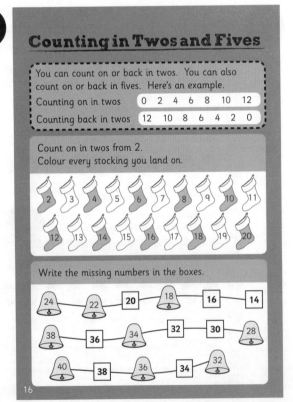

Write the missing numbers in the boxes.

24 22 **20** 18 **16** **14**
38 **36** 34 **32** **30** 28
40 **38** 36 **34** 32

You can help your child count on or back in twos by showing them how to do it with simple pairs of objects, e.g. pairs of shoes.

Count on in fives to put the numbers in the boxes.

Count on or back in fives on the grids below. Colour in the squares as you go.

Count on in fives from 15.

15	16	17	18	19	20	21	22	23	24
25	26	27	28	29	30	31	32	33	34
35	36	37	38	39	40	41	42	43	44

Count back in fives from 75.

75	74	73	72	71	70	69	68	67	66
65	64	63	62	61	60	59	58	57	56
55	54	53	52	51	50	49	48	47	46

Counting in Threes

You can count on or back in threes.
Here's an example.

| Counting on in threes | 3 6 9 12 15 18 |
| Counting back in threes | 18 15 12 9 6 3 |

Fill in the boxes to count on in threes.

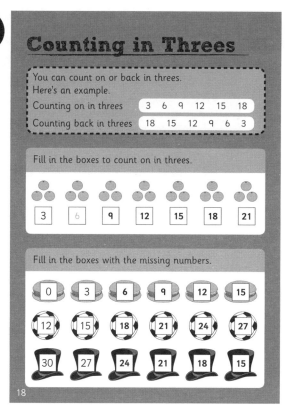

3 6 9 12 15 18 21

Fill in the boxes with the missing numbers.

0 3 6 9 12 15

12 15 18 21 24 27

30 27 24 21 18 15

18

Count on in threes from 21.
Draw lines between the numbers as you go.

Count on and back in threes from the numbers in the stars. Write the missing numbers in the boxes.

| 33 | 36 | 39 | 42 | 45 | 48 | 51 |
| | −3 | −3 | −3 | +3 | +3 | +3 |

| 51 | 54 | 57 | 60 | 63 | 66 | 69 |
| | −3 | −3 | −3 | +3 | +3 | +3 |

19

Counting in Fractions

You can count in halves:

Count from 1 to 3 in halves. $1 \quad 1\frac{1}{2} \quad 2 \quad 2\frac{1}{2} \quad 3$

Complete the number line by filling in the boxes.

$5 \quad 5\frac{1}{2} \quad 6 \quad 6\frac{1}{2} \quad 7 \quad 7\frac{1}{2} \quad 8 \quad 8\frac{1}{2}$

Count in halves to find how many full pizzas there are in each group.

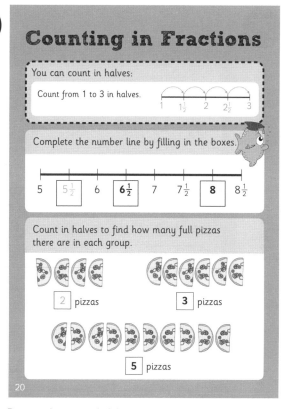

2 pizzas   3 pizzas

5 pizzas

20

You can also count in quarters:

Count from 6 to 7 in quarters. $6 \quad 6\frac{1}{4} \quad 6\frac{2}{4} \quad 6\frac{3}{4} \quad 7$

Fill in missing numbers on these number lines.

$3 \quad 3\frac{1}{4} \quad 3\frac{2}{4} \quad 3\frac{3}{4} \quad 4 \quad 4\frac{1}{4} \quad 4\frac{2}{4} \quad 4\frac{3}{4}$

$8 \quad 8\frac{1}{4} \quad 8\frac{2}{4} \quad 8\frac{3}{4} \quad 9 \quad 9\frac{1}{4} \quad 9\frac{2}{4} \quad 9\frac{3}{4}$

Count on in quarters by filling in the boxes.

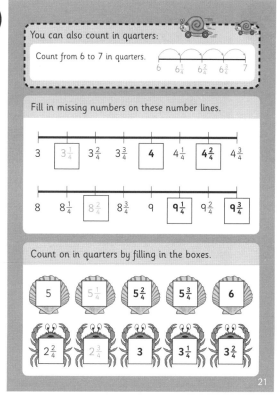

$5 \quad 5\frac{1}{4} \quad 5\frac{2}{4} \quad 5\frac{3}{4} \quad 6$

$2\frac{2}{4} \quad 2\frac{3}{4} \quad 3 \quad 3\frac{1}{4} \quad 3\frac{2}{4}$

21

Remind your child that you get two halves when you cut a whole into two equal parts.

Two quarters is the same as one half. So if your child has written $\frac{1}{2}$ instead of $\frac{2}{4}$, they've got the correct answer.

Ordering Numbers

Numbers can be bigger than, smaller than or equal to each other.

9 is bigger than 3
ten is equal to 10

17 is smaller than 30
forty-two is equal to 42

Circle the right numbers.

Which number is bigger?

5 or (7)

11 or (14)

(24) or 22

Which number is smaller?

(6) or 9

16 or (13)

(12) or 21

Write the answers in the boxes.

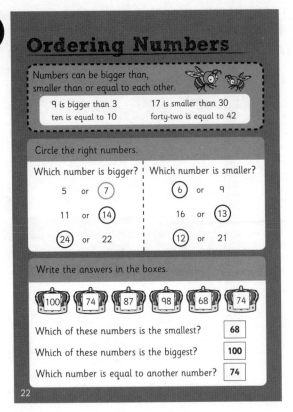

100   74   87   98   68   74

Which of these numbers is the smallest? **68**

Which of these numbers is the biggest? **100**

Which number is equal to another number? **74**

You can put numbers in order of size.

From small to big. ➡ 4   9   22   46   70

From big to small. ➡ 67   59   30   11   8

Put these numbers in order.

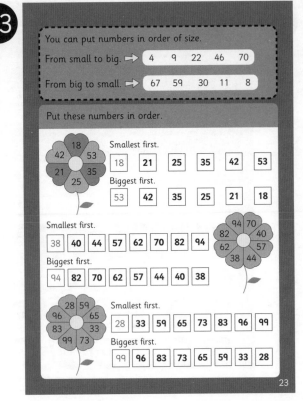

Smallest first.
18   **21**   **25**   **35**   **42**   **53**

Biggest first.
53   **42**   **35**   **25**   **21**   **18**

Smallest first.
38   **40**   **44**   **57**   **62**   **70**   **82**   **94**

Biggest first.
94   **82**   **70**   **62**   **57**   **44**   **40**   **38**

Smallest first.
28   **33**   **59**   **65**   **73**   **83**   **96**   **99**

Biggest first.
99   **96**   **83**   **73**   **65**   **59**   **33**   **28**

You can help your child with the questions on this page by encouraging them to cross out the numbers in the flowers once they have used them.

More or Less

A number can be one more or one less than another.

6 is one more than 5.   7 is one less than 8.

A number can be ten more or ten less than another.

40 is ten more than 30.   70 is ten less than 80.

Fill in the boxes with the missing answers.

1 more than 9	10	1 less than 13	12
1 less than 4	3	1 more than 15	16
1 more than 17	18	1 less than 19	18

Match the number on the ball to the right description.

10 more than 50.   (20)   10 less than 90.   (100)

(50)

10 more than 10.

(60)   10 less than 80.   (80)

10 more than 40.   (70)   10 more than 90.

If your child has difficulty understanding what 'one more' or 'one less' means, show them using small objects (like marbles) by adding one to a pile or taking one away.

Write down one more or one less than each number in the correct box.

33 ➡ 1 less **32**   47 ➡ 1 more **48**

51 ➡ 1 less **50**   68 ➡ 1 more **69**

85 ➡ 1 more **86**   100 ➡ 1 less **99**

Write the number that is ten less and the number that is ten more in the boxes.

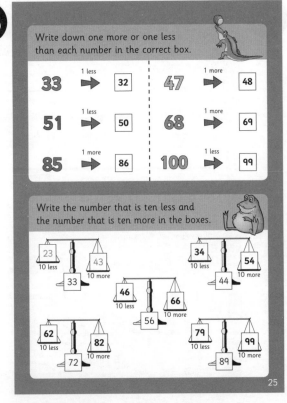

23 / 10 less / **43** / 10 more / **33**

34 / 10 less / **54** / 10 more / **44**

46 / 10 less / **66** / 10 more / 56

62 / 10 less / **82** / 10 more / 72

79 / 10 less / **99** / 10 more / 89

You can help your child with questions that ask for 10 more or 10 less than a number by showing them it's just like counting on or back in tens.

First, Second, Third

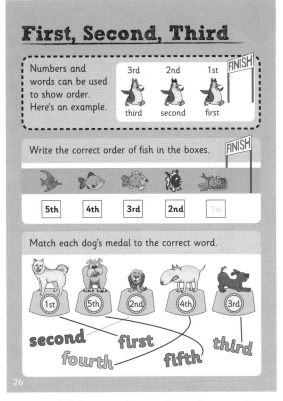

Numbers and words can be used to show order. Here's an example.

FINISH

| 3rd | 2nd | 1st |
| third | second | first |

Write the correct order of fish in the boxes.

FINISH

| 5th | 4th | 3rd | 2nd | 1st |

Match each dog's medal to the correct word.

1st 5th 2nd 4th 3rd

second first fourth fifth third

If your child struggles with understanding order, have a race with toy cars and get them to label the cars first, second and third.

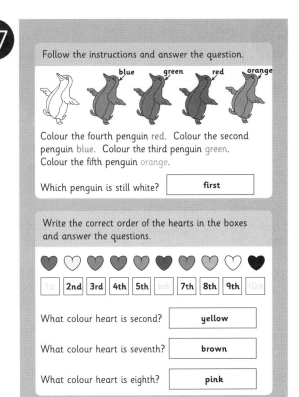

Follow the instructions and answer the question.

blue green red orange

Colour the fourth penguin red. Colour the second penguin blue. Colour the third penguin green. Colour the fifth penguin orange.

Which penguin is still white? **first**

Write the correct order of the hearts in the boxes and answer the questions.

| 1st | 2nd | 3rd | 4th | 5th | 6th | 7th | 8th | 9th | 10th |

What colour heart is second? **yellow**

What colour heart is seventh? **brown**

What colour heart is eighth? **pink**

If your child struggles with understanding order, next time you are in a queue get them to tell you what position you're in — first, second, third etc.

Money

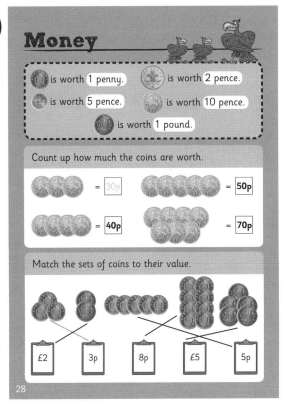

is worth 1 penny.
is worth 2 pence.
is worth 5 pence.
is worth 10 pence.
is worth 1 pound.

Count up how much the coins are worth.

= 30p   = 50p

= 40p   = 70p

Match the sets of coins to their value.

£2 3p 8p £5 5p

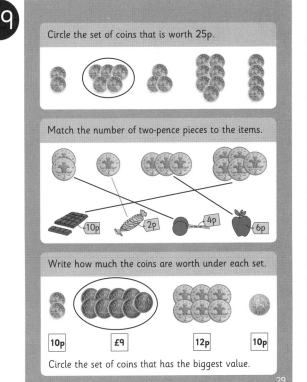

Circle the set of coins that is worth 25p.

Match the number of two-pence pieces to the items.

10p 2p 4p 6p

Write how much the coins are worth under each set.

10p   £9   12p   10p

Circle the set of coins that has the biggest value.

30

Mixed Counting Problems

Write the answers in the boxes.

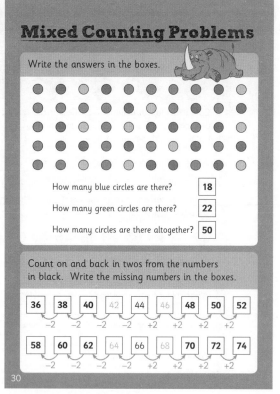

How many blue circles are there? **18**

How many green circles are there? **22**

How many circles are there altogether? **50**

Count on and back in twos from the numbers in black. Write the missing numbers in the boxes.

36	38	40	42	44	46	48	50	52
	−2	−2	−2	−2	+2	+2	+2	+2

58	60	62	64	66	68	70	72	74
	−2	−2	−2	−2	+2	+2	+2	+2

30

You can help your child count large numbers of objects by giving them extra practice — for example, ask them to count the different items on display in a supermarket.

31

Follow the instruction and answer the questions.

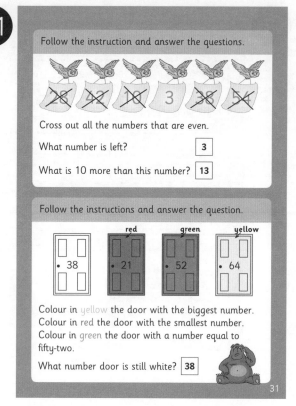

Cross out all the numbers that are even.

What number is left? **3**

What is 10 more than this number? **13**

Follow the instructions and answer the question.

• 38   red • 21   green • 52   yellow • 64

Colour in yellow the door with the biggest number.
Colour in red the door with the smallest number.
Colour in green the door with a number equal to fifty-two.

What number door is still white? **38**

31

If your child is confused by these pages, make sure they understand that the questions here are a mix of different types of counting problems.

32

Write the answers to the questions in the boxes.

55 18 17 43 41 66

Which of these numbers is one less than 19? **18**

Which of these numbers is one more than 40? **41**

Which of these numbers is ten more than 33? **43**

Which of these numbers is ten less than 65? **55**

Which of these numbers is one more than 16? **17**

Follow the instructions and answer the questions.

Count on from 97 in ones.
Fill in the numbers in the boxes below.

97	98	99	100	101	102	103	104

Count four forward from 97.
What number have you counted up to? **101**

Count back from 104 to 99.
How many did you count? **5**

32

MPCN12

Race to Bake the Cake

You'll need a counter for each player and a dice. Place your counters at the start point, and take it in turns to roll the dice once. Follow the instructions when you land on them.

8

9, 12, 15, 18, 21, 24

FINISH

twelve

55, 50, 45, 40, 35, 30, 25, 20

odd

12

38

45

10, 12, 14, 16, 18, 20

START

Count on in fives to put the numbers in the boxes.

5 ~~5~~ 20 50 ~~10~~ 30 35 15 45 40 ~~15~~ 25

Count on or back in fives on the grids below.
Colour in the squares as you go.

Count on in fives from 15.

15	16	17	18	19	20	21	22	23	24
25	26	27	28	29	30	31	32	33	34
35	36	37	38	39	40	41	42	43	44

Count back in fives from 75.

75	74	73	72	71	70	69	68	67	66
65	64	63	62	61	60	59	58	57	56
55	54	53	52	51	50	49	48	47	46

17

Counting in Threes

Fill in the boxes to count on in threes.

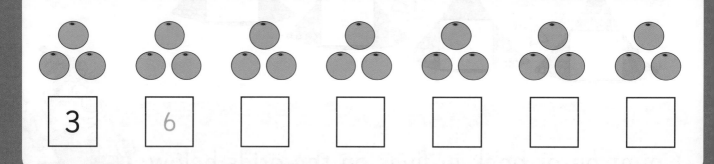

3   6

Fill in the boxes with the missing numbers.

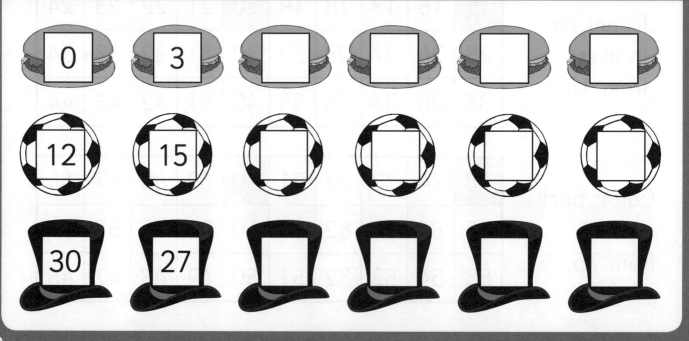

0   3

12   15

30   27

Count on in threes from 21.
Draw lines between the numbers as you go.

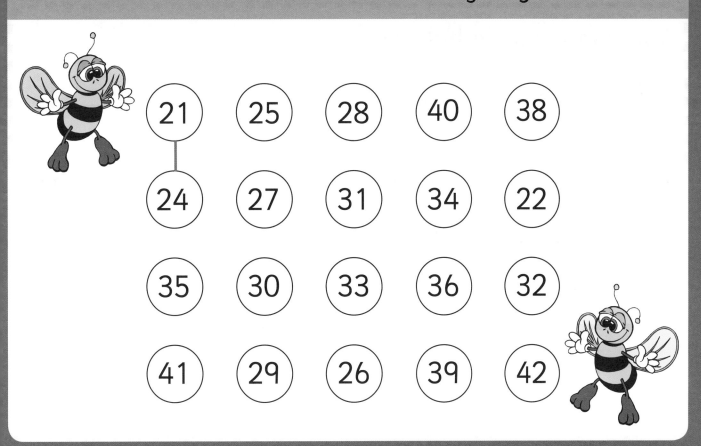

Count on and back in threes from the numbers in the stars. Write the missing numbers in the boxes.

		39	42	45		
−3	−3	−3	+3	+3	+3

		57	60	63		
−3	−3	−3	+3	+3	+3

Counting in Fractions

You can count in halves:

Count from 1 to 3 in halves.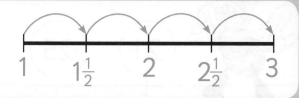

1   1½   2   2½   3

Complete the number line by filling in the boxes.

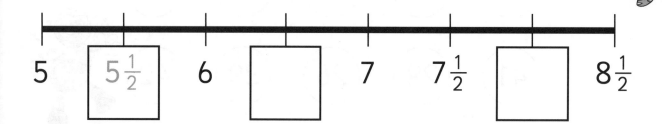

5    $5\frac{1}{2}$ 6   ☐   7 $7\frac{1}{2}$ ☐ $8\frac{1}{2}$

Count in halves to find how many full pizzas there are in each group.

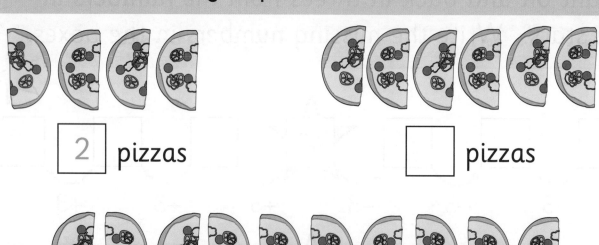

| 2 | pizzas |

| ☐ | pizzas |

| ☐ | pizzas |

You can also count in quarters:

Count from 6 to 7 in quarters.

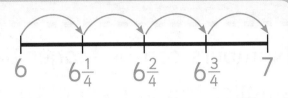

$6 \qquad 6\frac{1}{4} \qquad 6\frac{2}{4} \qquad 6\frac{3}{4} \qquad 7$

Fill in missing numbers on these number lines.

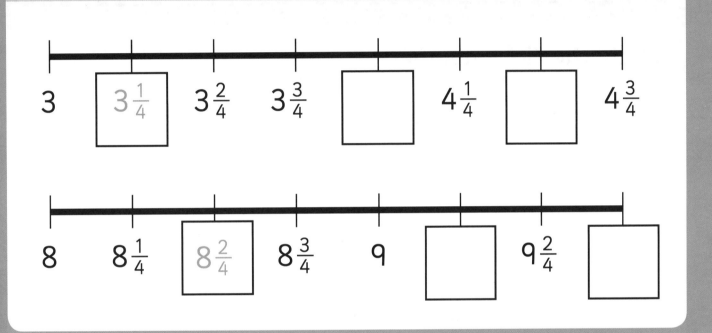

$3 \qquad 3\frac{1}{4} \qquad 3\frac{2}{4} \qquad 3\frac{3}{4} \qquad \square \qquad 4\frac{1}{4} \qquad \square \qquad 4\frac{3}{4}$

$8 \qquad 8\frac{1}{4} \qquad 8\frac{2}{4} \qquad 8\frac{3}{4} \qquad 9 \qquad \square \qquad 9\frac{2}{4} \qquad \square$

Count on in quarters by filling in the boxes.

$5 \qquad 5\frac{1}{4} \qquad \square \qquad \square \qquad \square$

$2\frac{2}{4} \qquad 2\frac{3}{4} \qquad \square \qquad \square \qquad \square$

Ordering Numbers

Numbers can be bigger than, smaller than or equal to each other.

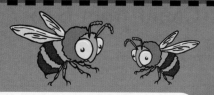

9 is bigger than 3
ten is equal to 10

17 is smaller than 30
forty-two is equal to 42

Circle the right numbers.

Which number is bigger?

5   or   (7)

11   or   14

24   or   22

Which number is smaller?

6   or   9

16   or   13

12   or   21

Write the answers in the boxes.

100   74   87   98   68   74

Which of these numbers is the smallest? ☐

Which of these numbers is the biggest? ☐

Which number is equal to another number? ☐

22

You can put numbers in order of size.

From small to big. ➡ | 4 9 22 46 70 |

From big to small. ➡ | 67 59 30 11 8 |

Put these numbers in order.

Smallest first.

| 18 | | | | | |

Biggest first.

| 53 | | | | | |

Smallest first.

| 38 | | | | | | | |

Biggest first.

| 94 | | | | | | | |

Smallest first.

| 28 | | | | | | | |

Biggest first.

| 99 | | | | | | | |

23

More or Less

A number can be one more or one less than another.

> 6 is one more than 5.   7 is one less than 8.

A number can be ten more or ten less than another.

> 40 is ten more than 30.   70 is ten less than 80.

Fill in the boxes with the missing answers.

1 more than 9 | 10 | 1 less than 13   [ ]

1 less than 4   [ ]   1 more than 15   [ ]

1 more than 17   [ ]   1 less than 19   [ ]

Match the number on the ball to the right description.

10 more than 50.

10 less than 90.

10 more than 10.

10 less than 80.

10 more than 40.

10 more than 90.

Write down one more or one less
than each number in the correct box.

33 → 1 less → ☐

47 → 1 more → ☐

51 → 1 less → ☐

68 → 1 more → ☐

85 → 1 more → ☐

100 → 1 less → ☐

Write the number that is ten less and
the number that is ten more in the boxes.

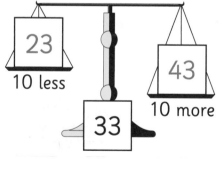

23
10 less

43
10 more

33

10 less

44

10 more

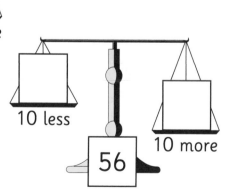

10 less

10 more

56

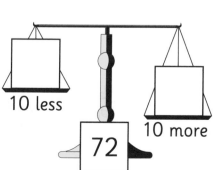

10 less

10 more

72

10 less

10 more

89

First, Second, Third

Numbers and words can be used to show order. Here's an example.

3rd
third

2nd
second

1st
first

FINISH

Write the correct order of fish in the boxes.

FINISH

☐ ☐ ☐ ☐ 1st

Match each dog's medal to the correct word.

1st   5th   2nd   4th   3rd

second   **first**   *third*

fourth   **fifth**

26

Follow the instructions and answer the question.

Colour the fourth penguin red. Colour the second penguin blue. Colour the third penguin green. Colour the fifth penguin orange.

Which penguin is still white?

Write the correct order of the hearts in the boxes and answer the questions.

| 1st | | | | | 6th | | | | 10th |

What colour heart is second?

What colour heart is seventh?

What colour heart is eighth?

Money

 is worth **1 penny.**   is worth **2 pence.**

 is worth **5 pence.**   is worth **10 pence.**

 is worth **1 pound.**

Count up how much the coins are worth.

 = 30p    = ☐

 = ☐    = ☐

Match the sets of coins to their value.

| £2 | 3p | 8p | £5 | 5p |

28

Circle the set of coins that is worth 25p.

Match the number of two-pence pieces to the items.

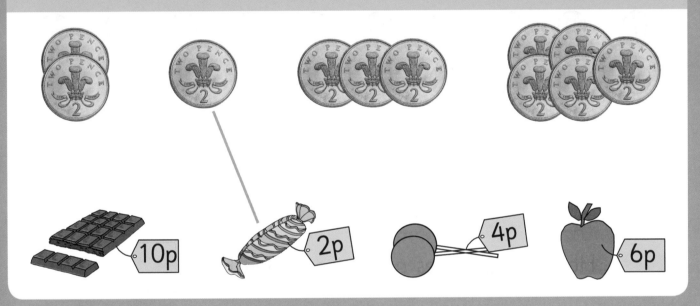

10p   2p   4p   6p

Write how much the coins are worth under each set.

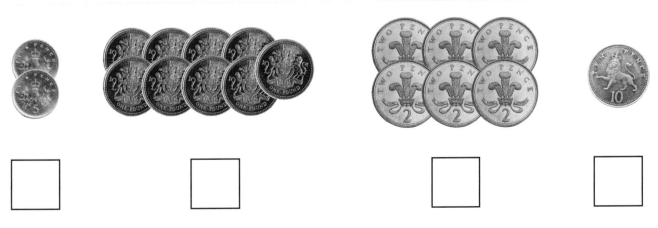

☐   ☐   ☐   ☐

Circle the set of coins that has the biggest value.

Mixed Counting Problems

Write the answers in the boxes.

How many blue circles are there? ☐

How many green circles are there? ☐

How many circles are there altogether? ☐

Count on and back in twos from the numbers in black. Write the missing numbers in the boxes.

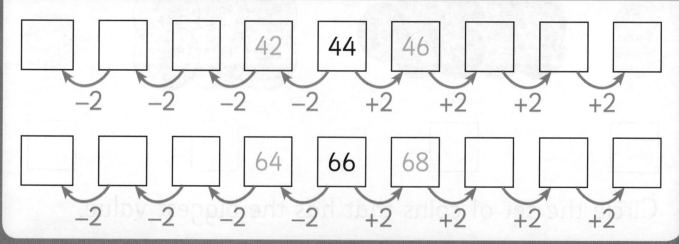

Follow the instruction and answer the questions.

28 42 10 3 38 54

Cross out all the numbers that are even.

What number is left? ☐

What is 10 more than this number? ☐

Follow the instructions and answer the question.

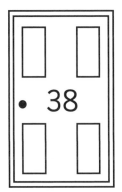 • 38   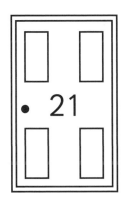 • 21   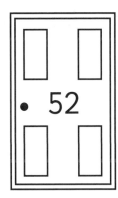 • 52   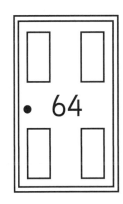 • 64

Colour in yellow the door with the biggest number.
Colour in red the door with the smallest number.
Colour in green the door with a number equal to fifty-two.

What number door is still white? ☐

Write the answers to the questions in the boxes.

55 18 17 43 41 66

Which of these numbers is one less than 19? ☐

Which of these numbers is one more than 40? ☐

Which of these numbers is ten more than 33? ☐

Which of these numbers is ten less than 65? ☐

Which of these numbers is one more than 16? ☐

Follow the instructions and answer the questions.

Count on from 97 in ones.

Fill in the numbers in the boxes below.

97							

Count four forward from 97.

What number have you counted up to? ☐

Count back from 104 to 99.

How many did you count? ☐

32